# OUTLAWS OF THE MARSH

# 水滸傳

ASIAPAC COMIC SERIES

# OUTLAWS OF THE MARSH

—— A humorous interpretation of the historical Chinese classic ——

# 水滸傳

Edited & illustrated
by Tsai Chih Chung
Translated by
Clara Show

ASIAPAC • SINGAPORE

*Publisher*
**ASIAPAC BOOKS PTE LTD**
629 Aljunied Road  #04-06
Cititech Industrial Building
Singapore 1438
Tel: 7453868
Fax: 7453822

First published May 1994

©ASIAPAC BOOKS, 1994
ISBN 981-3029-21-8

Cover design by Bay Song Lin
Typeset by Quaser Technology Pte Ltd
Body text in 8/9 pts Helvetica regular
Printed in Singapore by
Loi Printing Pte Ltd

# Publisher's Note

*Outlaws of the Marsh*, a new comic in Asiapac's **Hilarious Chinese Literary Classics** series, takes a look at seven of the 108 outlaws who sought refuge in Liangshan Marsh because of the "crimes" they committed.

Well-known Taiwanese cartoonist Tsai Chih Chung gives a contemporary account of the outlaws' experiences against the backdrop of a historical setting. Presented in a simple yet humorous way, this comic is both entertaining and informative.

If you have enjoyed our earlier titles *Journey to the West Books I and II*, and *Romance of the Three Kingdoms*, you will certainly like this edition of *Outlaws of the Marsh*.

# About the Editor/Illustrator

Tsai Chih Chung was born in 1948 in Chang Hwa County of Taiwan. He started drawing cartoon strips at the age of seventeen. In 1971, he worked as Art Director for Kuang Chi Programme Service. In 1976, he founded the Far East Production Company and the Dragon Cartoon Production Company. He produced two cartoon films entitled *Old Master Q* and *Shao Lin Temple*.

Tsai first got his four-box comics published in the papers and magazines in 1983. His funny comic cha-acters such as the Drunken Swordsman, Fat Dragon, One-eyed Marsh and Bold Supersleuth have been serialized in the papers in Singapore, Malaysia, Japan, Taiwan, Hong Kong, Europe and the United States.

Tsai was voted one of the Ten Outstanding Young People of Taiwan in 1985. He has received wide acclaim from the media and the academic circle in Taiwan.

The comic book *Sayings of Zhuang Zi*, published in 1986, was a milestone in Tsai's career. Within two years, *Zhuang Zi* went into more than seventy reprints in Taiwan and fifteen in Hong Kong and has to date sold more than one million copies.

In 1987, Tsai published *Sayings of Lao Zi, Sayings of Confucius* and two books based on Zen. Since then, he has published more than twenty titles, out of which ten are about ancient Chinese thinkers and the rest based on historical and literary classics. All these books topped the best sellers' list at one time or another. They have been translated into several other languages such as Japanese, Korean, Indonesian, Thai, French and Italian. Asiapac Books is the publisher for the English version of these comics.

Tsai is said to be the pioneer in the art of visualizing Chinese literature and philosophy by way of comics.

# Introduction

A widely-read book among lovers of Chinese classical novels, *Outlaws of the Marsh* tells the story of some 108 men who sought refuge on Liangshan Marsh after running into trouble with the law. The marsh became a famous hideout for these so-called outlaws.

Though fugitives in the eyes of the authorities, these men had committed crimes, ironically, in their bid to uphold justice. For example, Tiger Slayer Wu Song killed his treacherous sister-in-law because she had secretly poisoned and killed her husband in order to be with another man.

In another instance, Secular Monk Lu Zhishen fled the authorities after killing a high-handed butcher who preyed on a homeless old man and his daughter. The list of heroes who executed justice for the needy goes on.

In this comic version of the novel, seven of the more colourful characters of the Marsh are depicted. Through his creative ingenuity, Tsai Chih Chung presents a whacky and delightful twist to the original story and characters in this version. Readers will be treated to a very readable and humorous account of the exploits of these heroes. The essence of the novel is, however, not lost.

Here's wishing all readers many delightful hours of reading and of course, many more guffaws!

*Clara Show*

*Clara Show is a freelance translator*

# The Protagonists

## Wang Jin

He was an army instructor but unfortunately his father had offended his superior, Gao Qiu. Knowing that Gao Qiu would make life difficult for him, Wang Jin left Dongjing with his mother.

## Shi Jin

Also known as Tattooed Dragons, he became Wang Jin's disciple and mastered the use of 18 military weapons.

## Lu Zhishen

A former major in the garrison command, he was credited with rescuing an old man and his daughter from an evil butcher, Zheng. In a confrontation with Zheng, Lu Zhishen killed him and was forced to become a monk to escape arrest.

## Lin Cong

An arms instructor, Lin Cong was framed by an official who lusted after his wife. Banished to Cangzhou to be killed en route, he managed to escape to Liangshan Marsh.

## Wu Song

Although a drinker, he was an upright man. Besides being famous as a tiger slayer, he was also well-known for killing his adulterous sister-in-law and her lover, to avenge his brother's death.

## Song Jiang

A court clerk and a good samaritan, he was also a friend of the outlaws. When his mistress threatened to expose his links with the outlaws, Song Jiang killed her in his rage and hence, had to flee to Liangshan Marsh.

## Yang Zhi

Also known as the Green-faced Brute, he was provoked into killing a rascal who wanted to have his sword without paying for it.

# Wang Jin, the Army Instructor

An army trainer, Wang Jin realised too late the dire consequences of going on sick leave when his vengeful superior decided to take a roll call that very day.

# 王 進

There was a man named Gao Qiu who lived in Dongjing during the Song Dynasty. He loved kicking around with a ball...

As Gao Qiu was both a braggart and a flatterer, his master Duke Wang liked him a lot.

He's just a lazy bum who only knows how to play the ball!

You're a talent, Gao Qiu. It's a pity you indulge in all kinds of vices.

That's not true. I'm not all that bad.

My only regret in life is to have been born 900 years early.

Tell me what other things you haven't done.

Plenty, I would say.

Do you know that Maradona makes more than $10 million a year from playing soccer?

For one thing, I don't have a mistress and I've never gambled in Toto before.

One day, Gao Qiu was asked to deliver a letter to Prince Duan.

You're a good player. Stay here and work for me.

Thank you.

Prince Duan wants me to stay in his palace and play soccer for him!

That's great!

I'm going to have a big windfall.

What do you mean?

The "shoe decoy" tactic!

Good ball!

The transfer fee for a football player is US$30 million!

Fearing reprisals from Gao Qiu, Wang Jin left Dongjing, taking his mother with him.

# Shi Jin or Tattooed Dragons

The tattoo-covered, martial arts fanatic thought that he was invincible until he met Wang Jin. He became the latter's disciple and discovered there was more to martial arts than just fighting.

# 史 進

The young master of Shi Village was called Shi Jin. His nickname was Nine Tattooed Dragons.

He loved toying with the spear and pole, but never learnt any proper martial arts.

Watch this!

Get into the pocket!

Huh!

Ha, I've found a vulnerable point!

People will laugh when they see this.

Where's my vulnerable point?

Right here!

This is how you wield the sabre and forked spear together.

Concentrate on your training and leave my book alone.

Yes, Master.

And this is how you use the fork and knife.

He's afraid I may surpass him.

This is how you wield the twin poles!

A gongfu novel?!

The Eight Gods of Heaven

And this is how you use the small twin poles.

# Lu Zhishen, the Secular Monk

Forced by circumstances to enter the monastic order, he
found it difficult to give up his secular ways, in
particular, his love for meat and liquor. However he was
a kind person by nature.

# 魯智深

Lu Da, a garrison major in Weizhou, was an upright man with a great sense of justice.

Is something wrong? Why are you wailing?

My wife died and I tried to sell my daughter to give my dead wife a proper burial.

He enjoyed going to the tavern for drinks.

Woe begone ...

Butcher Zheng offered me 3,000 strings of cash. He wanted to take my daughter as his mistress, but his wife...

She drove us away. Now, Butcher Zheng keeps pressing us to return him the money.

Who's that wailing away? It really spoils my day!

It's a new entertainment item put up by the tavern

Outrageous! I can't allow something like this to go unpunished!

Please see that justice is done, Sir!

A glass of bitter wine

Not bad, eh?

You'll be the first to be punished.

The crime : Illegal selling of a human being!

Take this money and return to your hometown as soon as possible.

Sir, thank you for everything!

They still owe me money for food and lodging.

I'll pay for them.

You're a very kind and generous man, Sir.

It's just a small favour.

I wouldn't say so. Half a year of food and lodging adds up to quite a big sum.

Bill

1680 Taels

Meat Stall

The next day, Lu Da confronted Butcher Zheng.

You're not a man, Butcher Zheng! You can't even handle your wife and mistress!

I know of other men's mistresses who are into body-building.

As for my wife, she's into wrestling and judo.

31

You big bully! Take that!

!

When Lu Da realised that Butcher Zheng was dead, he quickly packed his things and fled from town.

Don't play dead! Get up and fight it out with me!

He's not pretending. He is dead!

There's been another murder case!

That's right.

How can you be so sure?

I've seen him play dead before.

A government official committed murder. No wonder he is unable to face anyone!

He has been doing this every night ever since he got himself a mistress.

WANTED MAN

Reward: 1,000 Taels

What are you looking for?

Shhh...

Do you know where they keep the liquor?

Liquor?

Let's look for the cook, but I don't know if he has the kind of wine that you want.

It doesn't matter as long as it's liquor.

A "brandy" nose – how about that?

I smell liquor.

!

You drank liquor secretly?

Of course not! I didn't!

But I know you have liquor with you somewhere.

No, I don't. Frisk me if you wish.

I knew it! You have liquor on your mind all the time!

Shaolin Temple is famous for its sinking bricks in one of its training rooms.

Wow! Is it an earthquake?

We can make the bricks sink in no time!

Come on, everybody!

Goodness! The main pillar has cracked!

Huuh! Bang!

Oh no, that's the end of me!

I'm going to kill this worthless disciple!

The floor bricks are intact, but there's a big hole in the roof.

Oh...

Confess! When you were in charge of supervising the construction, how much did you receive as bribe?

All right, I confess...

We can't let you stay here any more. Go and look for the Zen master Zhi Qing, in Dongjing.

Yes, Master.

Lu Zhishen is leaving. Let's get the food ready!

Get the chairs and lay the table!

Welcome! Welcome to our town!

They are holding a farewell party for me. I'm so touched...

I'm only passing through. I'm not here to sightsee.

Go on, leave now. We'll start the celebrations only after you've left.

Aren't you the monk from Long Fa Temple who is touring our island?

* Tokyo is also known as Dongjing in Mandarin

Lu Zhishen arrived at the Imperial Shrine in Dongjing.

Our vegetable garden attracts a lot of thieves. I want you to guard the garden.

Yes, Master.

All right, you may stay here. What kind of work can you do?

I'll drive these thieves away with my mighty fist!

I was once a garrison major and I was educated abroad. I'm good with weapons and I can fight well.

That will not drive them away.

It's said that foreign monks are good in prayers. I'll put you in charge of leading prayer sessions.

That's one thing I can't do.

Go away, you filthy little thieves! Shoo!

# Lin Cong or the Leopard Head

A sworn brother of Lu Zhishen, Lin Cong became
the victim of a conspiracy to separate him from his wife.
He was banished to another state but survived torture
by two bungling constables under instructions to kill
him en route.

# 林 沖

There lived an arms instructor in Dongjing called Lin Cong who was also known as Leopard Head.

Lin Cong had to teach the soldiers of the Imperial Army how to fight with the pole.

It's because he always scored a "leopard" (triple ace) whenever he tossed the dice.

A "leopard"! I've won again!

How dare you flirt behind my back!

Actually, I got my nickname for another reason.

Here, take this!

Ouch... Ouch!

I had smallpox when I was a kid and my whole head resembled a leopard's.

You're no match for me, my dear wife!

Lin Cong was an expert in martial arts. He was especially good with the pole.

One day, Lin Cong took his wife to a temple outside town.

This skill not only helps build up your body, but also comes in handy when you have to help your wife cook.

Huh!

Excellent!

Come on home and do your stuff.

Very well.

That's marvellous... really marvellous!

I'm so glad to have met someone who admires my pole-wielding skills.

Hold both ends tightly like this and one, two, one, two... This is how you roll out the noodle dough.

What I admire is not your skills...

but this weapon here.

51

I'm into all kinds of guns and weapons. I like to collect them.

I've collected quite a number of model guns — M16, AN47, KG9 — you name it, I have it.

I have a hobby too.

Oh?

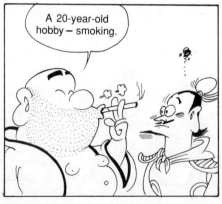

A 20-year-old hobby — smoking.

I'm Lin Cong, nicknamed the Leopard Head. I'm the 800,000-strong Imperial Army ...

You don't have to tell me. I know all about your past and future.

You mean you know how to tell fortunes?

Not really.

It's just that I have this book that gives a very detailed account of your life.

This is the one. The section on you starts from page 76, line six.

Outlaws of the Marsh

Get ready for the biggest shock of your life!

Do you have any idea whose wife you were trifling with?

No...

She's the wife of Lin Cong, the arms instructor of the 800,000-strong Imperial Army.

And do you know who I am?

No.

I'm the godson of Gao Qiu, commander of the 800,000-strong Imperial Army!

Please forgive me for my brashness! Let's go, dearie!

Official Gao kept thinking of Lin Cong's wife when he got home.

Still thinking of Lin Cong's wife?

Yes.

I can't understand why you like an old lady like her.

Well, she reminds me of my late mother.

I have a plan. We'll get Lin Cong to buy a knife and then ...

Good idea! But what if he refuses to get it?

This is indeed a good sword. How much is it?

Don't worry. I'll make sure he does.

Wait. Let me bargain the price down by three or four taels for you.

Get a knife, Sir. They're really cheap!

I can't lower the price any further.

Why not?

The best knives you can ever get!

It's a closing-down sale.

These are returned goods from overseas.

Three for just one unit of cash!

Because this sword costs only one unit of cash.

Sir, Lin Cong refused to plead guilty.

Torture him then.

No, no, we can't do that!

Why not?

Oh?

He has very solid backing. We can't do anything to him.

The law says that a third party must be present during interrogation of the prisoner and no torture of any kind is allowed.

Lin Cong was found guilty and given 20 strokes of the club. He was also banished to Cangzhou.

I don't want to ruin your life. Give me a piece of paper and a pen so that I can write the divorce letter.

It's not necessary. All prisoners convicted of felony will have their marriages declared null and void.

Pleased to meet you.

I have found another man to marry, so don't worry about me.

The two officials dared not plot against Lin Cong anymore, so he arrived at Cangzhou safely.

Hey you! Come over and kowtow to me.

The rule here is: If you have money, you'll be spared all punishments. Otherwise, you'll be thrown into the cell and be tortured.

Look! These scars are souvenirs from my days in the pugilistic world.

What blatant corruption! Have you no regard for the law?

This place is so out of the way, so what can the law do to me?

These marks don't make you more manly. Look at mine!

Big deal! These are just scratches.

I'll tell you what law!

The Encyclopaedia of Law

THE LAW

Amazing!

I got these from fighting with my wife.

Incredible!

The next day, two guards escorted Lin Cong to the barn.

You'll be spending winter in the barn. We have to be going.

Thanks.

He has gone inside. It's time to act!

Set fire to the hay and burn him alive!

You're making a fire to keep me warm? How thoughtful!

...

You'd better run while you can. We're under Gao Qiu's orders to kill you!

!

The great hero Wu Song gave us money to help you escape to Liangshan Marsh.

He's such a great man. I'm so touched!

You've got it all wrong.

According to the book, *Outlaws of the Marsh*, Wu Song cannot make his appearance unless you escape to Liangshan Marsh.

Try to find a boat for me to leave this place.

Sure! I'll get someone to take you to Liangshan Marsh.

No, no. It's not the "in" place for outlaws anymore.

So where do you want to go?

I'm thinking of going to the kabuki centre in Tokyo's Shinjuku.

I shot the arrow as a signal to the other party to send their boat over.

See how fast they responded.

Our sentry has been shot. We have to get him to the hospital right away!

As Lin Cong makes his trip to Liangshan Marsh with Zhu Gui, his story ends here.

The next character to appear on stage is the famous...

## Tiger Slayer, Wu Song.

# Wu Song, the Tiger Slayer

The famous tiger slayer became a murderer because the vampish wife of his midget brother had an extra-marital affair. A no-nonsense man, his only vice was drinking.

# 武　松

The story begins with a famous tiger slayer named Wu Song who lived in Clear River County.

Beer houses had been mushrooming all over Jingyang Ridge.

He possessed incredible strength and could subdue any tiger – even the "tigress" at home.

The most famous of them all was neither 'Three-Mug Chicken'...

Three-Mug Chicken

There are many tigers prowling in my house. I need your help.

No problem!

nor 'Three-Mug Rabbit'...

Three-Mug Rabbit

Please help me get rid of all these lizards and cockroaches.

Three-Mug Beer

but 'Three-Mug Beer' – naturally!

Ridge
impassable
after
three
mugs of
beer

Give me a plate of fried mussels to go with the beer.

What does the sign mean?

It means nobody can make it pass the ridge after drinking three mugs of beer.

Here you are.

That's an insult to me! Give me three mugs of beer!

Sure.

This plate is too small. Give me a bigger one.

Sure.

Good grief!

Here's a bigger plate.

Isn't that my younger brother?

Wu Song! It's me, Dalang!

Brother!

Brother!

Where is he?

Where did he go?

It's getting late. I'd better go home or my wife will scold me.

So, you've got a tigress at home.

Don't worry, I'll come with you and it'll be all right.

That's good.

Meet my brother, the famous tiger slayer.

Ooh...

You're so good-looking. Are you married?

She's not a tigress, she's a sex kitten.

Your wife is kind of flirtatious. You'd better keep an eye on her.

Go to work late and get home early to avoid trouble.

I will.

Dalang took his brother's advice – literally.

He goes to work at night and comes back in the morning.

A big bully named Ximen Qing lived in the same county. He speculated in property and also built houses.

XIMEN CONSTRUCTION

When I made money, I bought a villa in Mount Yangming.

When things were bad, I absconded to San Francisco.

And when I ran out of luck, I was extradited and thrown into jail.

Ximen Qing gave up his construction business to set up a pharmacy.

While out gallivanting one day, Ximen Qing was hit on the head by a pole.

Oh, I'm so sorry!

He had lots of gold, silver and jewels.

My, what a beauty!

I've made money through honest means.

Miss, would you like to be a movie star?

Can I?

Ten red pills and ten white pills. That will be $400.

XIMEN PHARMACY

Give me another bottle of this.

It's just for a low-budget movie entitled 'The Unfaithful Wife'.

It's a blue film!

The Unfaithful Wife.

Ximen Qing was in a daze after meeting Pan Jinlian.

Pan Jinlian embraced Ximen Qing.

Wang po, I want the woman next door. Can you help me?

Sure, as long as you have the money.

At Wang Po Hotel, the two started to...

3,300 taels of silver for the first time and if you want her to spend the night, double this amount.
In addition, you'll have to pay a tip of 30%.

No problem.

We're going to complain to the consumers association!

Where are the illustrations?

You're being too lazy!

It's a call girl service!

Wang Po Hotel

I got here as soon as she rang.

I'm sorry, steamy scenes are not allowed to be illustrated.

Restricted

Approved

Illustrator

Pan Jinlian met Ximen Qing at Wang Po Hotel whenever Dalang was not around.

Before long, everyone in town was talking about it.

Every one of us knew about it except Dalang.

Says who? I learnt about it from listening to San Mao, the storyteller and I simply love this segment.

San Mao tells a story

I'm going to catch the adulterous couple red-handed!

Dalang is here!

Your husband is here! I must find a place to hide!

But where?

Sorry, it's full house here. We're all her lovers too.

···

Pan Jinlian tried to poison Dalang again and this time, she succeeded.

HIS SOUL WITH US

Ah!

CREMATORIUM

I had his body cremated to get rid of any trace of evidence.

Brother, why did you die so suddenly?

Tell me, who killed you?

Where is Dalang? He owes us money for his drinks.

He's dead and cremated.

My dear brother, I died so tragically!

Why did you do that?

Someone told us he has fled to the States!

Did he feign death to avoid us?

It's not good to have a cremation lately.

I thought he wanted to know how I died.

I secretly took one of his bones home.

Dong! Dong!

Just and Honourable

The dog died after chewing on it. It proves that your brother died of poisoning.

This tiny bone isn't enough to crack the case!

Oh God, Dalang was such a kind man! Who would do such a thing to him?

Just and Honourable

It's cracked! It's cracked!

Oh God, Little Doggie was so adorable! Who would do such a thing to him?

Just and Honourable

Wu Song accused you of conspiring with Pan Jinlian to kill his brother. There's a heavy penalty for murder.

I don't know why the magistrate threw out my case, so I have to solve the murder case myself. Please be my witnesses.

As heavy as this?

Heavier.

Tell me how you killed your husband. I want details!

This heavy?

No. Much, much heavier.

I confess to killing him, but I can't tell you how I did it.

This should be heavy enough.

Right... almost.

If everyone knows the details, who's going to watch the movie?

The Murder of a Husband

Help! Help!

Punch!

Wu Song and Ximen Qing are fighting at the tavern!

Take this!

The law doesn't permit duels. We should stop them immediately.

They should settle their dispute in the court of law!

Someone has been killed!

He's dead!

Come over here if you're man enough!

Come over here if you have the guts!

I've landed on a dumpling seller!

91

Wu Song was sent to the court at Dongping to stand trial.

The proprietress of the shop was a member of the underworld.

It's getting late. Let's find a place to have dinner.

The waiter was a black man from Africa who also belonged to the underworld.

Many of the shops here are blacklisted.

Not everything here is as dark and dreary as you think.

I can see why. Even the walls are painted black.

At least your bill is on a white piece of paper.

93

97

# Song Jiang or Timely Rain

A wealthy and easy-going man, Song Jiang would go to extremes to help the needy. He married a young girl, was made a cuckold, and finally killed her to stop her from telling the authorities about his links with the outlaws of Liangshan Marsh.

# 宋 江

Song Jiang was a clerk of the county magistrate's court in Yuncheng. He wrote well and was by nature, a helpful man.

Song Jiang was the third in the family. He was dark and short. He scattered gold like dust and always did his best to help those in trouble.

He gave money to the poor and often helped others to solve their problems.

Have pity on a poor soul like me!

BEWARE OF FIRE

So famous was he throughout the county that everyone called him Timely Rain.

I hope this would help.

A 1,000-tael gold bar?!

Timely Rain!

On second thoughts, I might have overdone it.

Song Jiang loved making new friends with the gallant fraternity and was adept at all kinds of weapons.

He was also a big-eater and a good drinker.

A toast to you, Master Song.

With that small bowl of wine?

I would prefer to have a big basin of wine!

Song Jiang once helped an old lady who arrived at the county without any food or lodging.

The old lady wanted to let him have her daughter, Yan Poxi as his mistress.

Hey, can't you find a better looking girl to play the part of Poxi?

Sorry! All the good-looking ones have gone to take part in the Miss China Pageant.

Illustrator

Poxi was a frivolous girl of 18 or so, in the bloom of youth.

However, Song Jiang was only interested in martial arts, not women.

Because of their age difference, the couple had nothing much in common.

Besides, we are not of the same height either.

Master Song, you haven't visited my daughter for quite some time.

I'll be there tonight.

It's getting late. What are you doing here?

I've paid for the house and your allowance. I can come here anytime I like!

Sorry, I've only agreed to be your mistress in the day. I won't entertain you at night.

...

Song Jiang had an assistant named Zhang Wenyuan. His job was to deliver documents for Song Jiang.

Soon, he started delivering documents even in the night...

Song Jiang is back! Find a place to hide quickly!

You're back early.

Oh no, that must be my wife! I'd better find a place to hide!

Master Song is playing hide-and-seek with his assistant.

He doesn't even know his mistress has made a cuckold of him.

!

The chief of Liangshan Marsh, Chao Gai sent someone to give Song Jiang some gold to thank him for saving his life once.

That woman has caused me so much trouble!

!

So you've been making a cuckold of me!

Are you the court clerk, Song Jiang?

Yes.

...

No wonder I couldn't win in the lottery!

Everyone in the gallant fraternity calls me Timely Rain.

I can see why.

You little vamp! You're too much – I'll kill you!

Help!

Should I turn myself in or flee to Liangshan Marsh?

Should I let him escape to Liangshan Marsh or end his story right here?

**Outlaws of the Marsh** by Shi Nai-an

Since "The Lady Ghost" movies are so popular now, I suggest you make Poxi come back as a ghost to haunt Song Jiang.

Illustrator

Song Jiang put up his property for sale and got ready to flee from town.

For Sale

How much are you selling the house for?

Only 500 taels of silver.

This is too good to be true.

Maybe there's something illegal about the ownership.

Everything about the house is legal. It's the owner who had done something illegal.

107

Master, have you sold everything in the house?

Song Jiang sold all his belongings and left town hastily.

I have two pieces of antiques left unsold.

I suggest you reduce the prices drastically so that you can leave town soon.

Chief Chao has sent us here to escort you to Liangshan Marsh.

The big sale is now on! Buy this old manservant and you get the other one free! Only three units of cash!

I'm not going there. I'm heading for California, USA.

# Yang Zhi, the Green-faced Brute

After losing his job as an executioner, Yang Zhi
became a street peddler selling cleavers and swords.
He accidentally killed a notorious trouble-maker who
refuted his claim that his sword could cut through
copper and kill a man without leaving blood
on the blade.

# 楊　志

There lived a man in Guanxi named Yang Zhi who had a greenish patch on his face since birth. People of the gallant fraternity called him...

Though Yang Zhi looked extremely fierce, he was actually a kind-hearted man who loved children very much.

Green-faced Brute!

He's scary!

Open your mouth - let me see your tongue.

How sweet!

Nothing to worry about. You're just suffering from anaemia and over-secretion of bile.

Wah!

I just smiled at them, that's all.

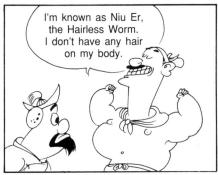

# Asiapac Comic Series (by Tsai Chih Chung)

### Art of War
Translated by Leong Weng Kam
    The Art of War provides a compact set of principles essential for victory in battles; applicable to military strategists, in business and human relationships.

### Book of Zen
Translated by Koh Kok Kiang
    Zen makes the art of spontaneous living the prime concern of the human being. Tsai depicts Zen with unfettered versatility; his illustrations spans a period of more than 2,000 years.

### Da Xue
Translated by Mary Ng En Tzu
    The second book in the Four Books of the Confucian Classics. It sets forth the higher principles of moral science and advocates that the cultivation of the person be the first thing attended to in the process of the pacification of kingdoms.

### Fantasies of the Six Dynasties
Translated by Jenny Lim
    Tsai Chih Chung has creatively illustrated and annotated 19 bizarre tales of human encounters with supernatural beings which were compiled during the Six Dyansties (AD 220-589).

### Lun Yu
Translated by Mary Ng En Tzu
    A collection of the discourses of Confucius, his disciples and others on various topics. Several bits of choice sayings have been illustrated for readers in this book.

### New Account of World Tales
Translated by Alan Chong
    These 120 selected anecdotes tell the stories of emperors, princes, high officials, generals, courtiers, urbane monks and lettered gentry of a turbulent time. They afford a stark and amoral insight into human behaviour in its full spectrum of virtues and frailties and glimpses of brilliant Chinese witticisms, too.

### Origins of Zen
Translated by Koh Kok Kiang
   Tsai in this book traces the origins and development of Zen in China with a light-hearted touch which is very much in keeping with the Zen spirit of absolute freedom and unbounded creativity.

### Records of the Historian
Translated by Tang Nguok Kiong
   Adapted from Records of the Historian, one of the greatest historical work China has produced, Tsai has illustrated the life and characteristics of the Four Lords of the Warring Strates.

### Roots of Wisdom
Translated by Koh Kok Kiang
   One of the gems of Chinese literature, whose advocacy of a steadfast nature and a life of simplicity, goodness, quiet joy and harmony with one's fellow beings and the world at large has great relevance in an age of rapid changes.

### Sayings of Confucius
Translated by Goh Beng Choo
   This book features the life of Confucius, selected sayings from The Analects and some of his more prominent pupils. It captures the warm relationship between the sage and his disciples, and offers food for thought for the modern readers.

### Sayings of Han Fei Zi
Translated by Alan Chong
   Tsai Chih Chung retold and interpreted the basic ideas of legalism, a classical political philosophy that advocates a draconian legal code, embodying a system of liberal reward and heavy penalty as the basis of government, in his unique style.

### Sayings of Lao Zi
Translated by Koh Kok Kiang & Wong Lit Khiong
   The thoughts of Lao Zi, the founder of Taoism, are presented here in a light-hearted manner. It features the selected sayings from Dao De Jing.

**Sayings of Lao Zi Book 2**
Translated by Koh Kok Kiang
   In the second book, Tsai Chih Chung has tackled some of the more abstruse passages from the Dao De Jing which he has not included in the first volume of Sayings of Lao Zi.

**Sayings of Lie Zi**
Translated by Koh Kok Kiang
   A famous Taoist sage whose sayings deals with universal themes such as the joy of living, reconciliation with death, the limitations of human knowledge, the role of chance events.

**Sayings of Mencius**
Translated by Mary Ng En Tzu
   This book contains stories about the life of Mencius and various excerpts from "Mencius", one of the Four Books of the Confucian Classics, which contains the philosophy of Mencius.

**Sayings of Zhuang Zi**
Translated by Goh Beng Choo
   Zhuang Zi's non-conformist and often humorous views of life have been creatively illustrated and simply presented by Tsai Chih Chung in this book.

**Sayings of Zhuang Zi Book 2**
Translated by Koh Kok Kiang
   Zhuang Zi's book is valued for both its philosophical insights and as a work of great literary merit. Tsai's second book on Zhuang Zi shows maturity in his unique style.

**Strange Tales of Liaozhai**
Translated by Tang Nguok Kiong
   In this book, Tsai Chih Chung has creatively illustrated 12 stories from the Strange Tales of Liaozhai, an outstanding Chinese classic written by Pu Songling in the early Qing Dynasty.

**Zhong Yong**
Translated by Mary Ng En Tzu
   Zhong Yong, written by Zi Si, the grandson of Confucius, gives voice to the heart of the discipline of Confucius. Tsai has presented it in a most readable manner for the modern readers to explore with great delight.

# Hilarious Chinese Classics by Tsai Chih Chung

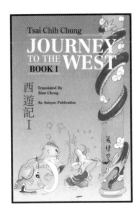

## Journey to the West 1

These books offer more than the all-too-familiar escapades of Tan Sanzang and his animal disciples. Under the creative pen of Tsai Chih Chung, *Journey to the West* still stays its course but takes a new route. En route from ancient China to India to acquire Buddhist scriptures, the Monk and his disciples veer off course frequently to dart into modern times to have fleeting exchanges with characters ranging from Ronald Reagan to Bunny Girls of the Playboy Club.

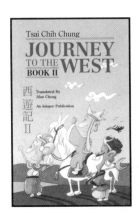

## Journey to the West 2

## Romance of the Three Kingdoms

Set in the turbulent Three Kingdoms Period, *Romance of the Three Kingdoms* relates the clever political manoeuvres and brilliant battle strategies used by the ambitious rulers as they fought one another for supremacy.

In this comic version, Tsai Chih Chung has illustrated in an entertaining way the four best-known episodes in the novel. Don't be surprised to see a warrior waving an Iraqi flag, a satellite dish fixed on top of an ancient Chinese building, and court officials playing mahjong or eating beef noodles, a favourite Taiwanese snack.

# Strategy & Leadership Series by Wang Xuanming

**Thirty-six Stratagems: Secret Art of War**
Translated by Koh Kok Kiang (cartoons) &
Liu Yi (text of the stratagems)
A Chinese military classic which emphasizes deceptive schemes to achieve military objectives. It has attracted the attention of military authorities and general readers alike.

**Six Strategies for War: The Practice of Effective Leadership**
Translated by Alan Chong
A powerful book for rulers, administrators and leaders, it covers critical areas in management and warfare including: how to recruit talents and manage the state; how to beat the enemy and build an empire; how to lead wisely; and how to manoeuvre brilliantly.

**Gems of Chinese Wisdom: Mastering the Art of Leadership**
Translated by Leong Weng Kam
Wise up with this delightful collection of tales and anecdotes on the wisdom of great men and women in Chinese history, including Confucius, Meng Changjun and Gou Jian.

**Three Strategies of Huang Shi Gong: The Art of Government**
Translated by Alan Chong
Reputedly one of man's oldest monograph on military strategy, it unmasks the secrets behind brilliant military manoeuvres, clever deployment and control of subordinates, and effective government.

**100 Strategies of War: Brilliant Tactics in Action**
Translated by Yeo Ai Hoon
The book captures the essence of extensive military knowledge and practice, and explores the use of psychology in warfare, the importance of building diplomatic relations with the enemy's neighbours, the use of espionage and reconnaissance, etc.

# Asiapac Comic Series :
# Contemporary Humour

### Battle Domestica

A satire about married life typified by a middle-aged couple who derive sadistic pleasure from mutual verbal assault.

Known as *Double Big Guns* in Taiwan, its Chinese edition has sold more than 400,000 copies worldwide.

### Sour Pack

There exist among us people who participate but are never committed; who are willing to give but attach more importance to what they get in return; who long for love but are terrified of being tied down.

Images of these people, their credo, and their lifestyles are reflected in the book. You may find in these cartoon characters familiar glimpses of yourself or those around you.

# Asiapac's Latest Title

## *100 Series* Art Album

# Forthcoming ...

## *100 Series* Art Album

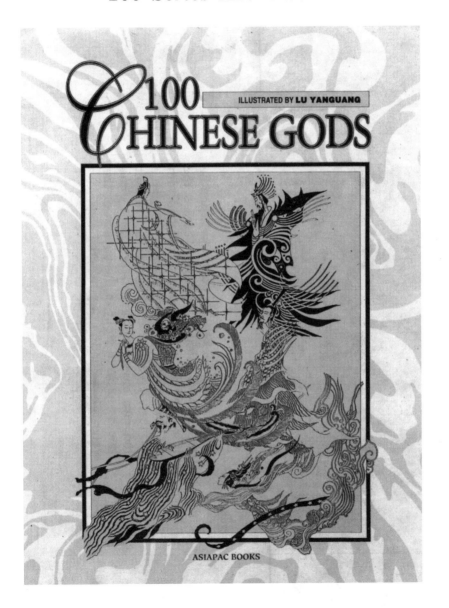

《亞太漫畫系列》

# 水 滸 傳

編著：蔡志忠
翻譯：丘惠芳

亞太圖書有限公司出版